How Animals Say Goodnight

Tuck in your little ones extra tight
tonight and please go to Amazon to leave
a review, the best way to support an
indie author, like me.

Thanks so much, Esther

Copyright © 2020 by Esther Pia Cordova
Illustrations by Anastasiya Provozina
All rights reserved. www.powerofyet.com

First Printing, 2021
ISBN 978-3-948298-16-6

Snakes do not blink or close their eyes,

But they figured out a way which is wise.

Clear scales cover the eyes of a snake,

It's hard to tell if it's asleep or awake.

Penguins sleep in cold and windy weather,

That is why they prefer to sleep together.

It helps them to stay safe and warm,

And this is normal penguin form.

Flamingos like standing on one leg to sleep,

This strange kind of balance is so hard to keep.

Do it yourself, and try closing one eye,

You might find yourself on the floor if you try.

Giraffes only sleep twenty minutes each day,

The rest of their time is spent munching away.

When they finally lie down, they curl up in a ball,

Which is cute as can be for a creature so tall.

Dolphins love to swim and play,

Until they need to sleep each day.

To breathe, they must come up to the top,

So they sleep using half of their brain and then swap.

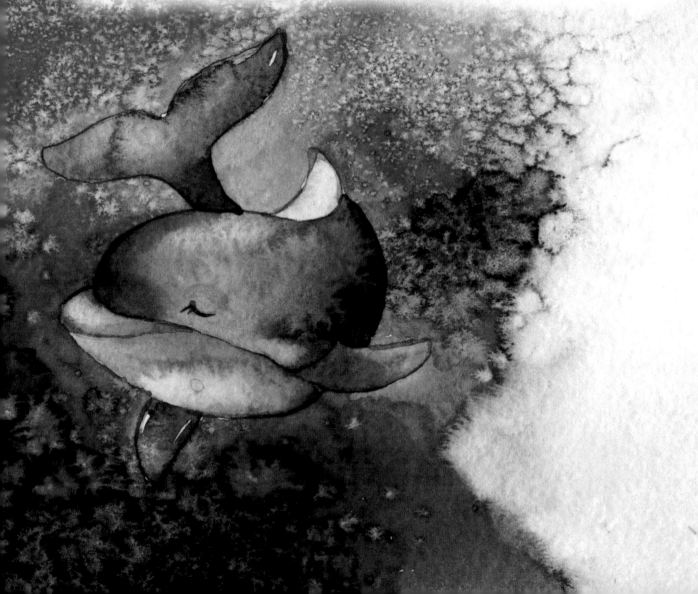

In beds made from sticks, twigs, and leaves you will see,

Our cute little friend, the chimpanzee.

He sleeps up to nine hours every day,

But he still has lots of time to play.

So big and so gentle are the elephants,

They spend most of their day eating plants.

This doesn't leave very much time for sleep,

Because elephants need more time to eat.

Sea otters sleep floating on their backs

Safe from the land animals' attacks.

They like to hold hands so they won't drift apart,

This proves that sea otters are really quite smart.

A walrus doesn't need sleep every day,

They sleep in a very unusual way.

They might swim three days straight and their eyes will not close,

But then sleep nineteen hours when they finally doze.

The sleepy snail hibernates inside its shell,

It sleeps for three years! That is quite a long spell.

You're lucky that you were not born as a snail,

So sleepy and slow with a wet, slimy trail.

Do not
disturb
3 years

The albatross doesn't get very much rest,

So sleeping is sometimes a difficult test.

It sleeps while it's flying up high in the air,

An impressive trick that is really quite rare.

Sperm whales need only short naps to thrive,

They sleep in a state that we call a "drift dive."

They give no response to a loud passing boat,

For they're sleeping so soundly as they float.

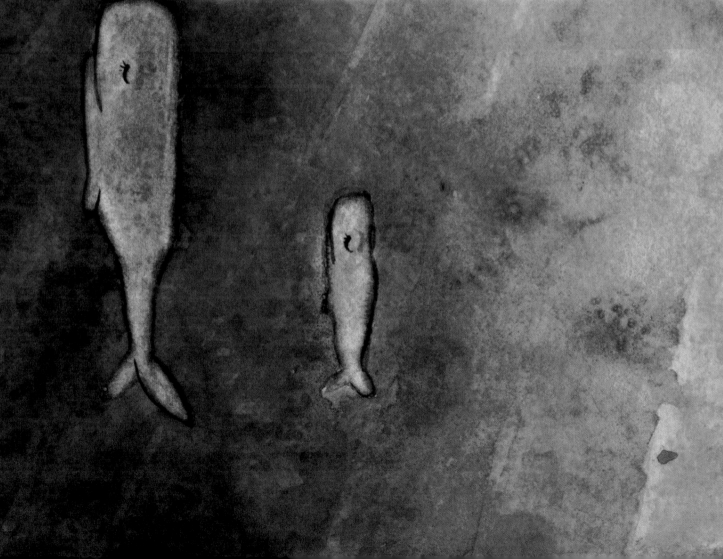

In winter, the brown bears hibernate,

An energy saving and deep sleeping state.

When the weather improves and food sources increase,

The bears' hibernation will finally cease.

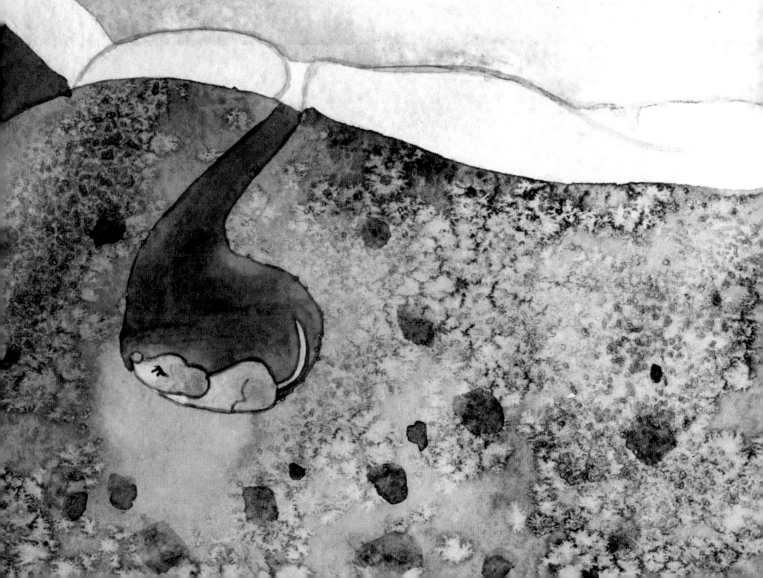

Ducks work together and sleep in rows,

The ducks in the middle keep both eyes closed.

The ones on the ends sleep with one open eye,

So if they see danger "quack quack," they will cry.

Bats sleep hanging upside down,

With their wings all wrapped around.

They like to hide out from the sun,

This looks like it could be great fun.

Animals say "good night" in their own special way,

Just like you at the end of another fun day.

So lie down and snuggle up warm in your bed,

And rest like the animals, my sleepy head.

Hungry Henry Series

My gift for you: Color and Grow
coloring book for **FREE** instead
of $6.99:

free.powerofyet.com/henry

Growth Mindset Series

I Can't Do That, YET

Enna is a girl who doesn't believe in herself and often utters the phrase "I can't do that!"

She develops a growth mindset throughout the story and learns to say, "I can't do that YET!".

A World without Failures

A world without mistakes.
Amazing or horrible?

After reading this story, children realize that mistakes are a good thing and are important for successful learning.

Your Thoughts Matter

Your child's mindset matters, *more than they realize.* 'Your Thoughts Matter' gives concrete examples of what different mindsets sound like in our heads.
'This is too hard; I'll never learn it.' vs *'It's meant to be hard; we grow by challenging ourselves.'*

Little Bears Can Do Big Things

Is it okay for boys to feel afraid? Is it okay for them to need help? Of course, it is.

A sweet father and son story about being brave.

Made in the USA
Middletown, DE
26 May 2024